Swim Team

Eleanor Robins

High Noon Books
Novato, California

Cover Design: Jill Zwicky
Interior Illustrations: Rick Hackney

International Standard Book Number: 1-57128-184-3

9 8 7 6 5 4 3 2 1 0
0 9 8 7 6 5 4 3 2 1

Contents

1 Why Are You Mad?...............................1

2 Go Out for the Team............................5

3 Last? 9

4 I'll Be Here 15

5 Let Rob Help You.............................19

6 Backup?...23

7 Better Than Last 31

8 Not the Best – Yet! 39

CHAPTER 1

Why Are You Mad?

Steve was at school. It was almost time for his first class to start.

He was in the hall next to his class. His best friend Ray was with him. The boys were talking to Val and Beth. Steve thought he might ask Val to go to a show.

Val said, "Look who just came out in the hall."

"Who?" Steve asked. He turned around to see who was there.

Val said, "It's Rob. He's on the school swim team."

Rob waved to them.

Beth said, "Let's go talk to him, Val. I know you want to."

"OK," Val said.

Val didn't say anything else to Steve. She just hurried over to Rob. Rob looked at Steve. He had a big smile on his face.

"He thinks he is so great. Just because he's on the swim team," Steve said.

"He's not so bad," Ray said.

"That's just what you think. He always wants to show off," Steve said.

"But he does swim well," Ray said.

"And he always talks about that over and over again," Steve said.

"So what? Let him," Ray said.

Steve said, "I can swim better than he can. I could beat him any time. Yet he thinks he is so great."

Ray said, "That's not why you don't like him. You are still mad about Jan. Because you both asked Jan to go out."

"I'm not mad about that," Steve said.

"Good. You shouldn't be. Because she didn't go out with you or him," Ray said.

"I didn't really want to take Jan out," Steve said.

But Steve knew he wasn't telling the truth.

At one time he had wanted to take Jan out. But not any more.

Ray said, "Why are you so mad at Rob?"

"I'm not mad at him. I just don't like him. He thinks too much of himself," Steve said.

Steve saw the girls walk into their classroom.

Then Ray said, "Oh, no."

"What?" Steve asked.

"Here he comes," Ray said.

Just what Steve needed. Now he would have to talk to Rob.

CHAPTER 2

Go Out for the Team

Rob walked up to them. He still had a big smile on his face.

"Hi," Rob said to the two boys.

"Hi," Ray said.

Steve just looked at Rob.

Rob looked over at Steve. He said, "Did I take the girls away from you?"

That mad Steve mad. "No, you didn't. Is that all you came over here to say?" he asked.

"No. Stay away from those girls," Rob said.

Now he didn't have a smile on his face.

"And who is going to make me?" Steve asked.

"Maybe I will," Rob said.

Ray said, "Cool down, guys. We don't want to get in trouble."

"You're right," Rob said.

Steve knew Rob didn't want to get into trouble. The coach might take him off the swim team.

Steve said, "You think you are so great. Just because you are on the swim team. Well, you're not so great. I can swim better than you."

"Then why aren't you on the swim team?" Rob asked. He looked mad.

"Anyone who can swim can be on the swim team. You don't have to have a lot of skill. You just have to want to be on the team. And I don't want to be," Steve said.

Rob got very red in the face. He said, "It does take a lot of skill."

"No, it doesn't," Steve said.

"Then show me it doesn't," Rob said.

"I'll be glad to. How?" Steve said.

"Show me how easy it is to make the team. Go out for the team," Rob said.

"OK. Maybe I will," Steve said.

Rob said, "Then I'll see you at practice today after school. But one more thing."

"What?" Steve said.

Rob said, "You can't just be on the team. You have to be good enough to swim in a meet." Then he walked off.

Ray said, "Why did you say that you didn't need skill to be on the team? That wasn't a nice thing to say."

"Maybe I don't feel so nice right now," Steve said.

"Are you really going out for the team?" Ray asked.

Steve said, "No. But I may show up for practice. Then I can show him I swim better than he does."

CHAPTER 3

Last?

Steve was on his way to swim practice. Ray was with him.

"Are you sure you want to do this?" Ray asked.

Steve was sure he did. He said, "I'm sure. It shouldn't take me long. I'll show Rob I swim better than he does. Then he'll know he isn't so great."

"Rob isn't such a bad guy. Don't you want to think about this some more?" Ray said.

"No. Are you still going with me?" Steve said.

"Yeah," Ray said.

Steve went to the locker room. He put on his swimsuit. Then he went to the pool. Ray went with him. They walked over to the coach.

"OK for me to swim with the team?" Steve asked.

The coach said, "Sure. Do you plan to try out for the team?"

Why did he have to try out? All he had to do was be able to swim. And he could do that.

"Maybe. I'm not sure yet," Steve said.

But Steve was sure. He didn't want to be *on* the team. He just wanted to swim *with* the team.

He wanted to show Rob how good he was. That he was as good as any boy on the team. Maybe better.

"OK for me to watch?" Ray asked.

The coach said, "Sure. Just don't get in the way."

Ray went to stand next to the pool.

The coach said to Steve, "First we do some warm-ups. Then you can swim some laps with the team. That way you can see how we do things."

"Fine," Steve said.

The coach told the team who Steve was. And that he might try out for the team. Most of the boys knew Steve.

Rob had a big smile on his face. Steve didn't

know why he was smiling. He felt that Rob didn't want him on the team.

The team did some warm-ups. Then the coach called Steve over to him.

The coach said, "You can race with five members of the team. Have you dived from a starting block before?"

"No," Steve said. He was sure that it would be easy to do.

Steve didn't think the coach had to show him what to do. But the coach showed him anyway.

Then the coach called five boys over. He told them Steve would swim some laps with them. Rob was one of the five boys.

The five boys got on their starting blocks.

The boys got on their starting blocks.

Then Steve got on his starting block. Steve was sure he could swim as fast as the other boys.

The coach blew his whistle. All the boys dived into the water. The other boys got off to a fast start. Steve did not.

Steve swam as fast as he could. But that wasn't fast enough. Too soon the race was over.

Steve was very surprised. He had come in last.

Last? How could he have come in last?

CHAPTER 4

I'll Be Here

The coach said, "You swim well, Steve. But you need to work on your dives."

Steve knew how to dive. He was a good diver. Why did the coach think he needed to work on his dives?

The coach said, "Same six boys. Now swim two laps."

The boys got out of the pool. They were walking to their starting blocks.

Rob walked by Steve. He had a big smile on

15

his face. He said, "I'll be glad to help you learn to dive, Steve." Then he laughed.

Steve would show Rob. He would do better when they swam two laps.

The coach said, "Steve, be sure to touch the other side. Then start back."

The boys got to their starting blocks. The coach blew his whistle.

The boys dived into the water. Steve got off to a better start. He swam as fast as he could.

He wasn't too far behind. He was almost to the other side. The five boys quickly turned and started back. Steve was sure they hadn't touched the side.

Steve touched the side. Then he turned and

started back. He swam as fast as he could.

Last again. But this time he was very far behind.

The coach said, "You swim well, Steve. But you need to work on your turns."

Steve looked at Rob. He had a big smile on his face.

Rob said, "Want me to help him with his turns, Coach?"

Help from Rob? That was the last thing Steve wanted.

Steve said, "I can't stay now. I have to go."

He'd had enough swimming for one day. He got out of the pool.

"Will you be here tomorrow, Steve?" the

coach asked. Steve wished the coach had not asked him that.

Rob answered for him. He said, "Sure he will be here. Won't you, Steve?"

Rob had that same big smile on his face.

"Yeah. I'll be here," Steve said.

Steve hurried to the locker room. Quickly he put on his school clothes. And he was out of there.

CHAPTER 5

Let Rob Help You

Steve went outside. Ray was waiting for him at the door.

"Did you hear what Rob asked the coach?" Steve said.

"About helping you with your turns?" Ray asked.

"Yeah. How dare he ask the coach that? He didn't even touch the side. And he wanted to help me," Steve said.

"You're wrong," Ray said.

"Why did you say that?" Steve asked.

"Rob did touch the side. I saw him," Ray said.

"He couldn't have. Not one of them did," Steve said.

Ray said, "They all did. I saw them. They are all just real good at turns."

Steve still didn't think they could have touched the side that fast. But he didn't say anything more.

Ray said, "Are you really going to practice tomorrow?

Steve said, "I have to. Thanks to Rob. But that's the last one. Do you want to swim with me?"

Ray said, "Not me. I like to swim. But that looks too much like work. But I'll go with you and watch."

"Thanks," Steve said.

Ray didn't say anything. They walked for a while and didn't talk.

Then Steve said, "So what happened to me? Why was I last all the time?"

Ray said, "It was what the coach said. You need to work on your dives. And your turns."

"I know how to dive," Steve said.

"But not how to dive when you race. That's how they got in front of you. Your dives were not at all like their dives," Ray said.

Steve said, "I'll do better tomorrow. I'll

show Rob I'm a better swimmer."

But now Steve wasn't so sure he was. Maybe Rob was right. Maybe he really was a better swimmer than Steve.

CHAPTER 6

Backup?

It was the next day. It was time for swim practice to start. Steve went to the pool. Ray went with him. Rob was the first boy they saw.

"You did come back," Rob said. He looked surprised.

Steve said, "Yeah. I came back. I said I would."

"Staying for all the practice? Or are you leaving when you come in last?" Rob said.

Steve said, "I'm staying. And don't count on

me coming in last."

"You still here just to watch?" the coach asked Ray.

"Yeah. That still OK?" Ray said.

"Sure is. But swim with us. We'll be glad to have you," the coach said.

"Thanks. But I'll just watch," Ray said.

The team did some warm-up exercises. Next they did some warm-up laps on their own.

Then the coach said, "Time to race. We'll do the backstroke first. Just one lap. Steve, can you do the backstroke?"

Steve said he could.

The coach told Steve to race first. Then he told Rob to race with Steve. He told four more boys to race with them. He told the other boys to watch.

"Do you know how to push off, Steve?" the coach asked.

"Yeah," Steve said.

The coach blew his whistle.

Steve pushed off. He swam as fast as he could. But it was too late. The other boys had gotten off to a good start. Steve had not.

"Stay in your own lane, Steve," the coach said.

Too late. He bumped into the boy in the next lane. Just his luck that it was Rob.

Steve came in last again. Rob had a big smile on his face. But he didn't say anything.

He bumped into Rob in the next lane

The coach told six more boys to race. Then he said, "Steve, watch these boys. And see how they push off."

Steve didn't want to watch them. He wanted to go. But he did watch them.

Then they all had to dive in and race. Steve had to race with the same five boys. Why did he have to race with Rob?

Steve dived off too soon. So they had to start over.

Rob said, "That's one way to try to win. It's not fair. But it's one way to try to win."

The coach blew his whistle. The race started over again. And Steve came in last again.

He could hardly wait for practice to end. He

would tell the coach he would not be back.

He did not have to be No. 1. And he did not have to be No. 2. It would even be OK to be No. 3. But last? No way.

The coach told them to get with a partner. He told Rob to be Steve's partner. Steve had to swim first. And Rob would tell him what he did wrong.

Rob yelled at Steve a lot. It seemed all Steve did was wrong.

Steve could hardly wait until it was Rob's turn to swim. And his turn to yell.

But Steve couldn't find anything wrong. So he just told Rob to swim faster.

It was time for practice to end. The coach called Steve over to him. He said, "Steve, you are a very good swimmer."

Steve had always thought he was a very good swimmer. But now he wasn't so sure.

The coach said, "But you need a lot a work. We have a lot of meets left. Work hard and I might use you as a backup."

Who did the coach think he was? He wasn't a backup.

Steve was so mad he could hardly talk. But he said, "Thanks. But I can't be on the team. I don't have time to practice every day."

"Too bad, Steve," the coach said.

Steve heard Rob laugh.

Rob said, "I knew he would quit. I told you he would."

Steve knew he couldn't quit. He could not let Rob think he was a quitter.

"I'll work something out, Coach. And I'll be here. For all of the practices," Steve said.

CHAPTER 7

Better Than Last

It was the next day. Steve was at the pool. Ray was with him. They were the first boys there. Practice didn't start for 30 minutes.

Ray said, "You don't want to be here. So why did you come?"

Steve said, "I had to come. I can't let Rob think I'm a quitter."

"You didn't have to come so early. Why did you?" Ray asked.

"I have to get better. There is only one way

31

to do that. I have to practice a lot," Steve said.

Could he learn to swim better? And maybe swim better than Rob? He didn't know. But he would never find out unless he tried. He would try to do the best he could. And that was really all that counted.

Ray said, "Good luck. I'll see you later." Then Ray left.

Steve went to talk to the coach. He said, "I thought about what you said. I want to try to be a backup for the team. So I want to learn as much as I can."

"Glad to hear that," the coach said.

Steve said, "So what do I need to work on?"

"How to dive well. How to turn well. And

how to push off from the wall," the coach said.

"What do I need to work on first?" Steve asked.

"Your dive. A good dive can cut your swim time. It will give you a better chance to win," the coach said.

He showed Steve how to do a good dive. And then Steve began to work on his dives.

"Your last dive was better than your first. Keep working on it. And I think you will soon dive well," the coach said.

Some other boys came in.

The coach told Steve to swim some laps. He went to talk to the other boys. Steve saw Rob. Rob looked surprised to see Steve.

All the boys swam on their own for a while. Then the coach blew his whistle. He said, "Time to race. Race with the same boys as yesterday."

Steve would have to race Rob again. And they were to race first.

The boys got on their starting blocks. The coach blew his whistle for the race to start. Steve dived into the water. His dive was much better. It had helped for him to practice his dives.

Steve did not do well. He came in last again. But he wasn't as far behind the others as before. So he knew he had done a little better.

Steve worked very hard. He got very tired. He was glad when practice was over.

The next day he went to practice early again.

He needed to swim as much as he could. And he needed to get help from the coach.

"What do I need to work on first, Coach?" Steve asked.

The coach said, "You need to push off from the wall better. If you push off badly, you will fall behind in the backstroke."

The coach showed Steve how to push off. Then Steve worked a lot on his own.

Soon it was time for practice to start. the boys did some warm-up laps. Then the coach blew his whistle. He said, "Today we are going to work on the backstroke."

Rob walked up to Steve. He said, "Don't bump me today."

Rob said, "Don't bump me today."

Steve felt his face get very hot. He knew most of the boys had heard Rob.

The Coach heard Rob, too. He said, "Rob, you can work with Steve on his backstroke. And show him how to stay in the right lane."

Rob's face got red. Then he showed Steve how to stay in the right lane. He helped Steve with his backstroke, too.

Then the coach said, "Time to race. Race the same boys you did yesterday."

So Steve had to race Rob again. The coach told them to race first.

Rob said, "I helped you. So you had better swim better today."

Steve was surprised to find that Rob wanted

him to swim better.

The coach blew his whistle. Steve pushed off from the wall. He knew he had gotten a better start. And he thought his backstroke was better.

Steve tried to do the best that he could. He came in fifth. It wasn't good. But fifth was better than last.

CHAPTER 8

Not the Best – Yet!

Steve went outside. Ray was waiting for him.

"How did it go today?" Ray asked.

"Better. I didn't come in last," Steve said.

Just then Rob walked out the door. He said, "I helped him."

"You helped him?" Ray said.

"Yeah," Rob said. He looked at Steve.

"Yeah. He did," Steve said.

"I didn't think you two guys liked each other," Ray said.

"We don't. The coach told me to help him," Rob said.

"Maybe you will get along better now. I sure hope so," Ray said.

Rob said, "No way. He always wants to take out the girl I want to take out."

That made Steve mad. Rob knew that wasn't true. He said, "You have that wrong, Rob. And you know it. You always want to take out the girl I want to take out."

Rob's face got red. At first he looked too mad to talk. But then he said, "I don't think so. I wanted to take Jan to a show first. And then you wanted to take her to a show. I wanted to take Beth to a game. And now you want to take her to a game."

"Beth? You want to take Beth out?" Steve said.

"Yeah. And you can't stop me," Rob said.

"I don't want to stop you. I want to take Val out," Steve said.

"Val? I thought you wanted to take Beth out," Rob said. Then he looked over at Ray.

He said, "*You* must be the one who wants to see Beth."

Ray said, "Not me. I want to take Jan to a show. The girl who wouldn't go out with either one of you."

The three boys had talked about the girls they wanted to take out. But did the girls want to go out with them? Maybe yes. Maybe no.

Ray said, "Now maybe the two of you can get along."

Rob said, "No way. Steve thinks too much of himself."

"I think too much of myself?" Steve yelled at him.

Rob said, "Yeah. You're always saying how great you are at something. Like swimming. You think you swim better than anyone else."

Steve said, "So now we know I can't. But you're the one who thinks too much of himself."

"Why do you think that?" Rob asked. He looked surprised.

Steve thought about it. Rob thought it was

42

great to be on the swim team. And it was. Not everyone had the skill to be on the team. It took more than just knowing how to swim.

Maybe Rob didn't think too much of himself after all.

It had turned out that they didn't want to take out the same girl. And Rob had helped him at practice. And Ray didn't think Rob was so bad. Maybe Rob wasn't so bad after all.

Steve said, "Maybe I am wrong. I'm willing to try to be friends. How about you?"

Rob said, "OK. I'll give it a try. And I'll even help you at practice. And the coach won't have to tell me to do it."

Steve said, "Thanks. Then I will see you

tomorrow at practice."

For the next three weeks Steve worked hard at practice. Rob helped him a lot, too.

Then the big day came. Steve would race in his first meet. But it was also the last meet of the year.

Steve did the backstroke. And he had to swim four laps. He didn't win. He came in fifth. But that was better than last.

Steve was not a winner yet. But he would still work hard. There was always next year. And Steve was sure he would do better then. One day maybe he would even come in first!